THE BEST OF
The Charlatans

**26 of The Charlatans' best-loved songs, spanning their whole career.
Carefully transcribed in guitar tablature, complete with guitar chord boxes.**

Representation: Steve Harrison Management

© 2005 Faber Music Ltd
First Published in 2005 by Faber Music Ltd
3 Queen Square, London WC1N 3AU

Arranging and engraving by Artemis Music Ltd (www.artemismusic.com)
Cover photograph © Sarahphotogirl/Retna
Printed in England by Caligraving Ltd
All rights reserved

ISBN 0-571-52447-8

**To buy Faber Music publications or to find out about the full range of titles available, please contact your
local music retailer or Faber Music sales enquiries:**

Faber Music Ltd, Burnt Mill, Elizabeth Way, Harlow, CM20 2HX England
Tel: +44 (0) 1279 82 89 82   Fax: +44 (0) 1279 82 89 83   sales@fabermusic.com   fabermusic.com

Contents

Can't Get Out Of Bed

Words and Music by Timothy Burgess, Martin Blunt, Robert Collins, Jon Brookes and Mark Collins

Don't let it stand out in the cold, don't let it fall into a hole with

some-one you know. Don't let it out in the cold, don't

Can't come in the road,_____ you fill in the holes___ and ru - in your clothes.

Can't get out of bed_____ there's noth-ing and no-one's com-ing ov-er to me___ there.

There's noth-ing that you want-ed to be_____ or

with Gtr. fig. 2.

want-ed to be___ I want-ed to be,___

want-ed to be___ and want-ed to be.___

Crashin' In

Words and Music by Timothy Burgess, Martin Blunt, Robert Collins, Jon Brookes and Mark Collins

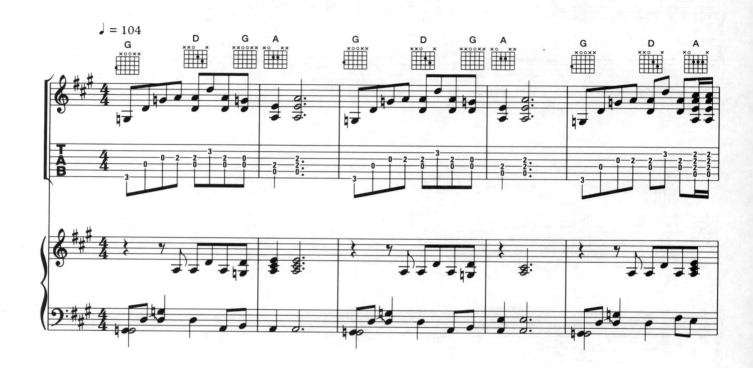

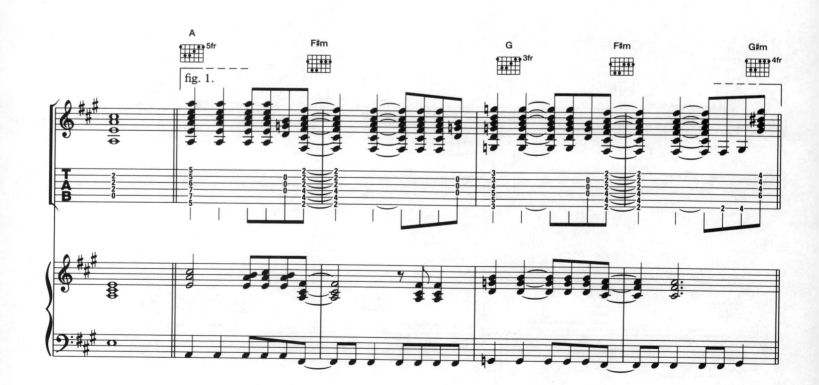

See me— I can feel it com-ing a - round.—

1.2.3.

4.

[E]

Yeah,——————— yeah.

[E] repeat ad lib. to fade

Happen To Die

Words and Music by Jon Baker, Jon Brookes, Robert Collins, Martin Blunt and Timothy Burgess

you do the same on me?

me?

Elec. Gtr. 2

Elec. Gtr. 1

Touch_ by._

Gtr. 1 w/light overdrive
Gtr. 2 w/dist.

Solo

Organ solo ad lib.

Chorus

If you hap-pen to die I won't be there._____ If you

hap-pen to leave_ there in - der to re-main_ there would you do the same on me?_____

you...

Here Comes A Soul Saver

Words and Music by Timothy Burgess, Martin Blunt, Robert Collins, Jon Brookes and Mark Collins

Here comes a soul sa - ver_____ on your re-cord play - er, float - ing a - bout in the dust.__
2. Tell me I'm sweet-er_____ than your bro-ken lead - er, I'll take the smooth with the rough.

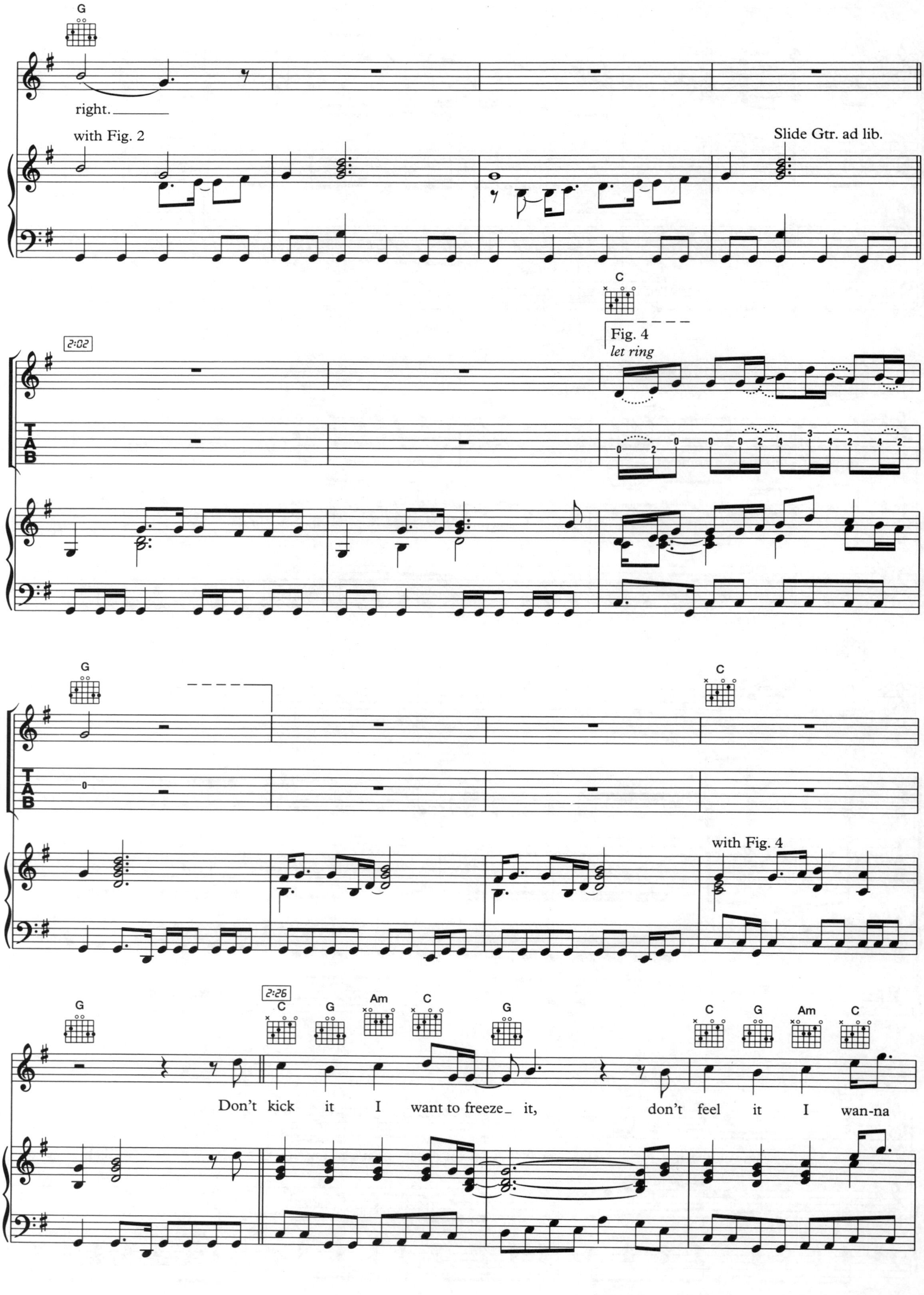
G
right.
with Fig. 2
Slide Gtr. ad lib.
2:02
C
Fig. 4
let ring
TAB
G
C
with Fig. 4
G
2:26
C G Am C G
C G Am C
Don't kick it I want to freeze_ it,
don't feel it I wan-na

How High

Words and Music by Timothy Burgess, Martin Blunt, Robert Collins, Jon Brookes and Mark Collins

high   oh! I   can kiss the sun,   run a   min-ute mile   while you hitch hike   love

buy   what I've done be-fore   I want to   o - pen up an - oth - er door I'm going to

high   oh! I   can kiss the sun,   run a   min-ute mile   while you hitch hike   love

Gtr. fig. 1 ad lib.

Jesus Hairdo

Words and Music by Timothy Burgess, Martin Blunt, Robert Collins, Jon Brookes and Mark Collins

Boxes are Kbd. chords adapted for Gtr.

Leave us____ I'm__ in hea - ven and I can't be - lieve I'm watch - ing you__ when
Fix our____ hands to - ge - ther when I surf, a - no - ther wave comes right, don't

Gtr. 2.
Standard
tuning

Rhy. fig. 1.

ev - ery - thing you float up - on__ comes down too soon.
wan - na cry, know what I need, oh choose your words.

Je - sus____ hair - do, I __ mean we
Je - sus____ hair - do, I __ mean we

Sing your song when - ev - er, can't you see you're catch-ing some-thing I need. ___

cont. sim.

Get your-self to - ge-ther now, you're com-ing, com-ing out of the phase. ___

[B]

Impossible

Words and Music by Martin Blunt, Jon Brookes, Timothy Burgess, Mark Collins and Anthony Rogers

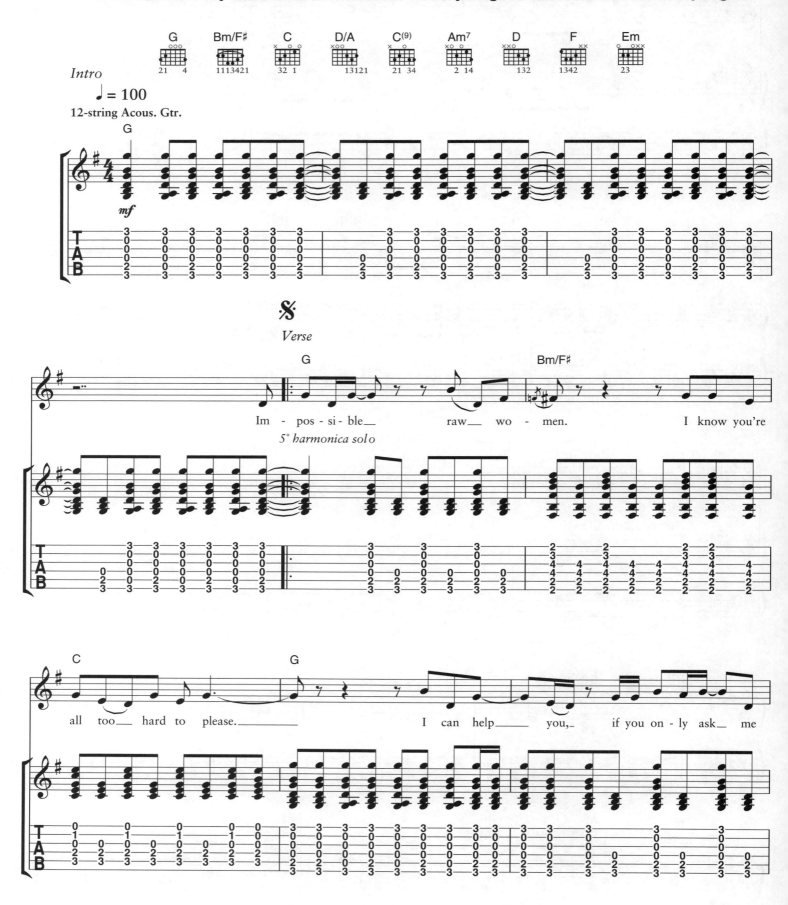

Bridge

Play 5 times then
D.%. al Coda

Don't

✆ *Coda*

Play 4 times

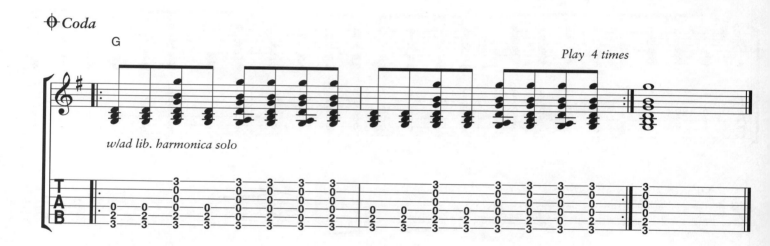

w/ad lib. harmonica solo

Verse 2:
Don't need you to need me to need my freedom
My freedom is a vision you seek
And the place you disappear to
Is the place I wish to be
I beg you, instill you
Don't treat it like some kind of joke
This song is, kind lady, my only hope.

Verse 3:
You can't kill an idea just 'cause it's raining
Keep it in the family, keep it in the kid
You know they're handing out free tickets
This big old boat is-a-starting to sink
The whole world is getting hungry
And it ain't memories you need from me
And if memories are all you need from me
You're a hard act to please.

Verse 4:
I miss you and it's lonely
I admit I can hardly sleep
Y'know he looks like a plastic surgeon
Just look at him – he's a piece
This whole world is like a postcard
Easy lost and easy to reach
And if this is where you're going
I will surely leave.

Verse 5:
Ex-impossible raw woman
You know you're oh so hard to please
Your new friend he seems to love it
I hope he cries himself to sleep
She will fool you
Destroy you
Disappear, without so much as smoke
This song is, cruel lady, my only hope.

Judas

Words and Music by Timothy Burgess, Jon Brookes, Martin Blunt, Mark Collins and Anthony Rogers

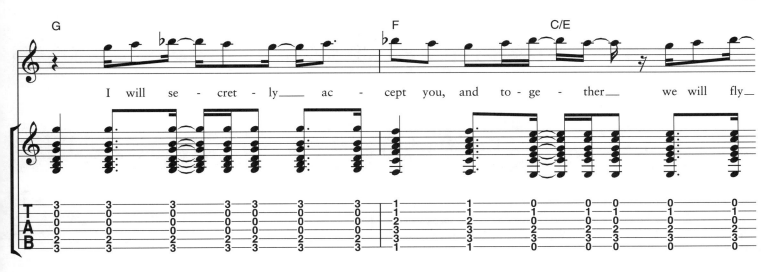

I will se - cret - ly___ ac - cept you, and to - ge - ther___ we will fly___

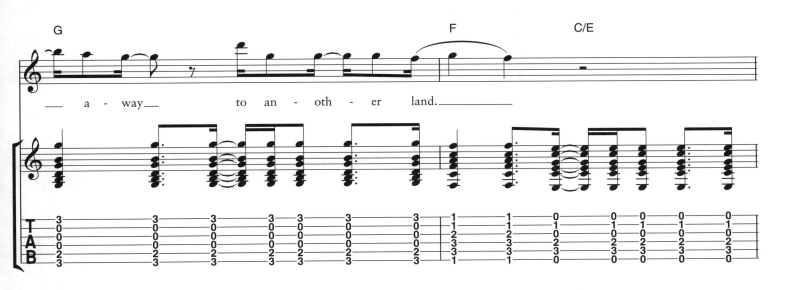

___ a - way___ to an - oth - er land.___

𝄋
Chorus

Ooh,___ can you tell me how you feel to - day.___ I found___

Synth sounds ad lib.

Just Lookin'

Words and Music by Timothy Burgess, Martin Blunt, Robert Collins, Jon Brookes and Mark Collins

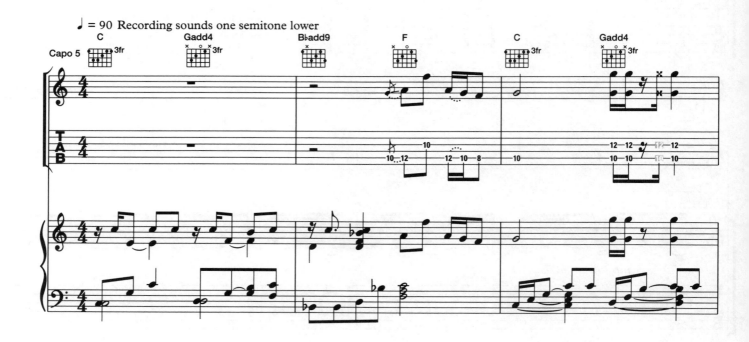

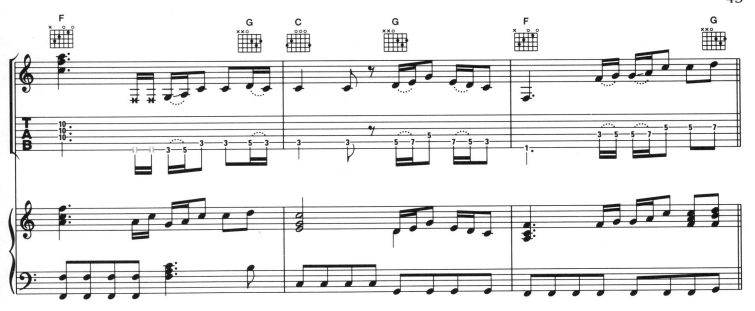

I'm just look-in' to see what I'm miss-ing,__ you start-in' the ri-
I'm just look-in' to see what I'm miss-ing,__ you start-ed the ri-

- ot,__ ten green bot-tles fly down from the hill - side,__ you're too young to stay qui-
- ot,__ pret-ty soon I'll be blow - in' to match you,__ it's too dull and too qui-

- -et.___ Find a seat on your own___ train,___ I wan-na
- -et,___ I bet you___ talk a-bout free - dom,___ and then

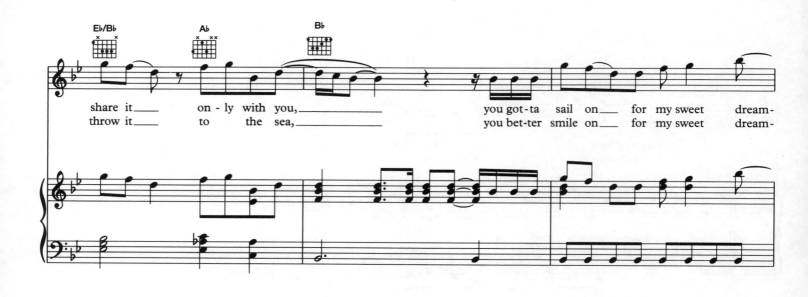

share it___ on-ly with you,_____ you got-ta sail on___ for my sweet dream-
throw it___ to the sea,_____ you bet-ter smile on___ for my sweet dream-

- -er, I'll ne-ver take it a-way___ from you._____
- -er, you'll ne-ver take it a-way___ from me._____

Yeah we stand with our hands in the air,_____ and we're feel - ing so good 'cause we care,

_____ and we're freak - ing a - bout_ in the bush,_____ feel - ing good feel-ing high_ it's a rush,

count me in 'cause I don't wan-na work,_____ in no place in the whole u-ni-verse._____

Just look-in',___

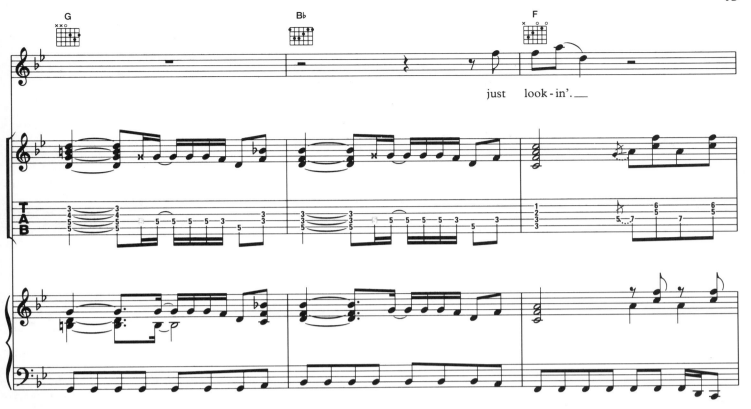

just look-in'. ___

look - in', ___

just look - in'. ___

Just When You're Thinkin' Things Over

Words and Music by Timothy Burgess, Martin Blunt, Robert Collins, Jon Brookes and Mark Collins

Just when you're think-ing things ov - er,
and you need a set of vows,

I found you soak-ing in li - quid,
I found you there in your

Just when you're think-ing things ov - er,
oh yeah, you found your set of vows,

Right now___ where do you come from,___ kick up, go find your

sing a-ny-more, I'm com-ing home.

repeat ad lib. to fade

Love Is The Key

Words and Music by Timothy Burgess, Jon Brookes, Martin Blunt, Mark Collins and Anthony Rogers

Loving You Is Easy

Words and Music by Timothy Burgess, Jon Brookes, Martin Blunt, Mark Collins and Anthony Rogers

Outro

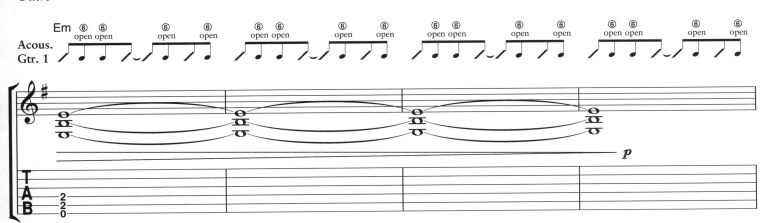

Piano arr. for Acous. Gtr. 1

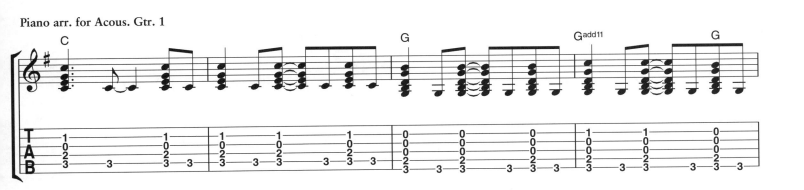

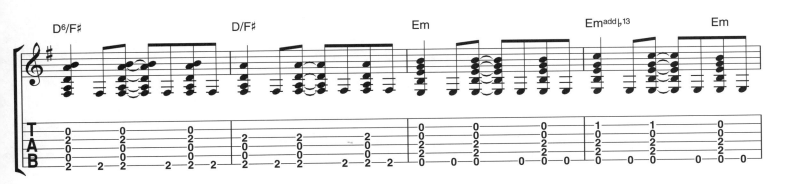

A Man Needs To Be Told

Words and Music by Timothy Burgess, Jon Brookes, Martin Blunt, Mark Collins and Anthony Rogers

To Coda ⊕

D.%. al Coda

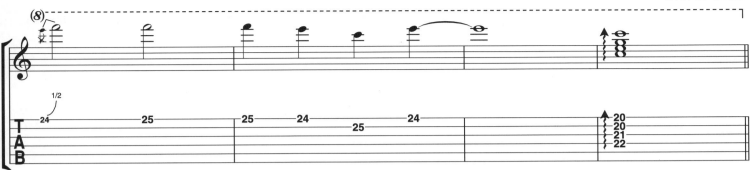

⊕ Coda

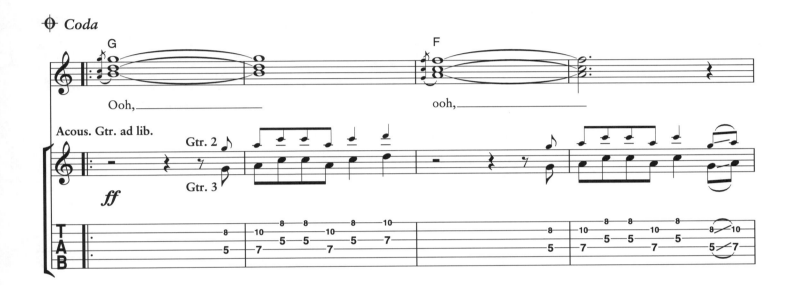

Ooh,_____ ooh,_____

Acous. Gtr. ad lib.

Gtr. 2

Gtr. 3

ff

ooh,_____ ooh.

Verse 2:
A young boy once told me
I will be an old man and I am only 15
It wasn't part of the plan
It wasn't part of the dream
Ever wonder how much the man
Who wrote 'White Christmas' made?
How evolution began
The revolution was fake.

Verse 3:
A man needs to be told
There is a war going on
There is a war going on
There is a war going on
A man needs to be told
There is a truth in his eye
There is a rest in the dawn
There is a point to his life.

My Beautiful Friend

Words and Music by Martin Blunt, Jon Brookes, Timothy Burgess, Mark Collins and Anthony Rogers

Verses 1 & 2

Bridge 1

3. My___ beau - ti - ful friend,_____ I swear I a - dore___ you, Ain't no wo - man deep e - nough._

(Verse 4 see block lyrics)

Outro

Do you ev-er get this feel-ing_____ we're sup-posed to car-ry on._____

Acous. Gtr. 1

Gtr. 2 cont. ad lib. sim.

Verse 2:
Let me sleep and I will feed you when your hungry
Forever live inside of me
Through the holes in my pockets of my clothes
High, as high as an angel
I'll stand here beside you
Love is all we need.

Verse 4:
I could leave us, I could leave us a paining
Our lives are-a-changing
Solid gold
I couldn't and I wouldn't evade you
Don't you know it I can save you
I'll do it on my very own.

North Country Boy

Words and Music by Timothy Burgess, Martin Blunt, Robert Collins, Jon Brookes and Mark Collins

Hey coun-try boy, _____ hey coun-try boy. _____ What are you

good to you___ if I could I'd make you hap-py, if I had a son I'd be good to my dad-dy, who
It-chy and Scrat-chy come run-ning up the al-ley, if you'll be good I'll be good to your dad-dy, who
good to you___ if I could I'd make you hap-py, if I had a son I'd be good to my dad-dy, who

loves you but I bet it's not___ the same___ as your___ north coun-try

3rd time to Coda

boy.

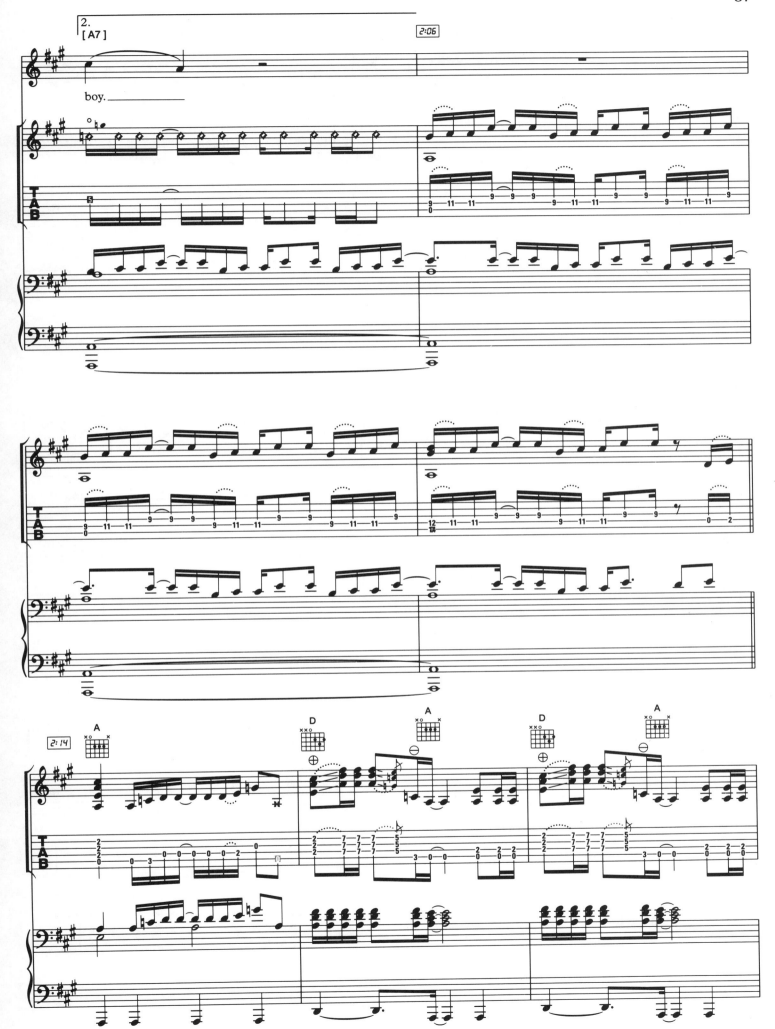

D.%. al Coda

⊕ CODA

3. What do you

boy.

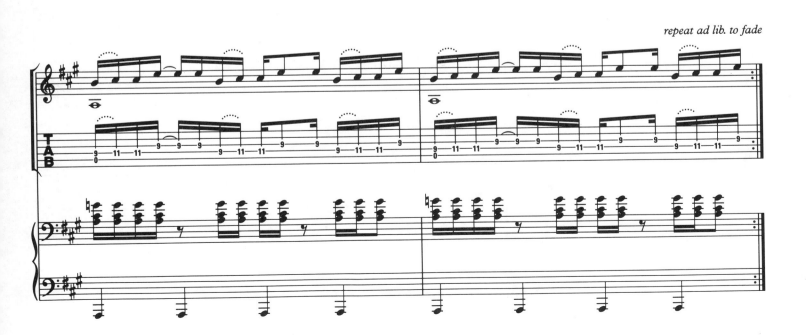

One To Another

Words and Music by Timothy Burgess, Martin Blunt, Robert Collins, Jon Brookes and Mark Collins

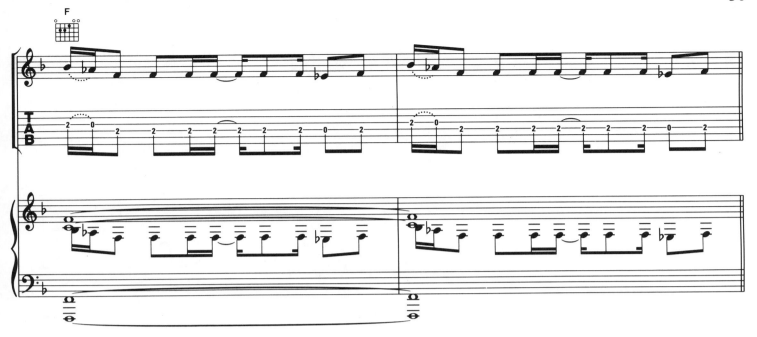

One to an-

-oth - er, sis-ter and a bro-ther, and I'm chang - in' the way____ that you feel.____

Pleased to meet you, hope I ne-ver see you, I'll be at ease,__ watch-in' you sleep, watch-in' you

smile.

fig. 1

I hear our day is com - ing, ___ gets sweet-er ev-ery year. To-mor-row's gon-na be too ea - sy and ___ to-day's ___ gon-na be too near. Trust is for be-liev - ers and love can keep the faith. I don't need you, I can't buy you, I can't

Over Rising

Words and Music by Jon Baker, Jon Brookes, Robert Collins, Martin Blunt and Timothy Burgess

he's the on-ly god who got you____ down,

ease your-self on____ me.____

D.%. al Coda

⊕ CODA

Patrol

Words and Music by Timothy Burgess, Martin Blunt, Robert Collins, Jon Brookes and Mark Collins

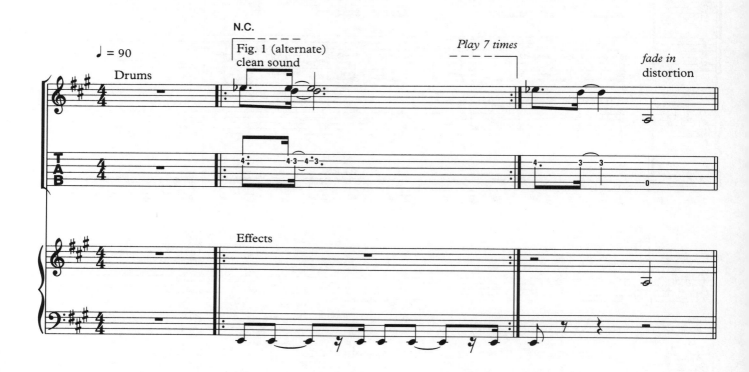

108

Less of the mad-ness, of the mad - ness, of the mad-ness, _ of the mad____

_ mad. _

Sun comes up, ___ sun comes down ___ on a wave ___ to get the ~ ~ ~ ~ to

Sproston Green

Words and Music by Martin Blunt, Robert Collins, Timothy Burgess and Jon Baker

This one knows, she comes and goes, ___

D.% al Coda *with repeats*

CODA

And ev-ery - thing_ she stole was mine.___

You got this one,_____ I got no - one._

The Only One I Know

Words and Music by Martin Blunt, Robert Collins, Timothy Burgess, Jon Brookes and Jon Baker

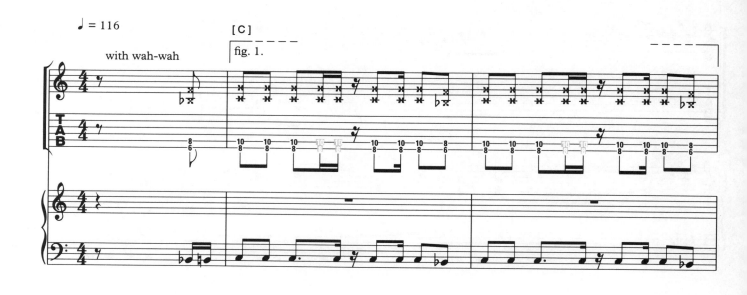

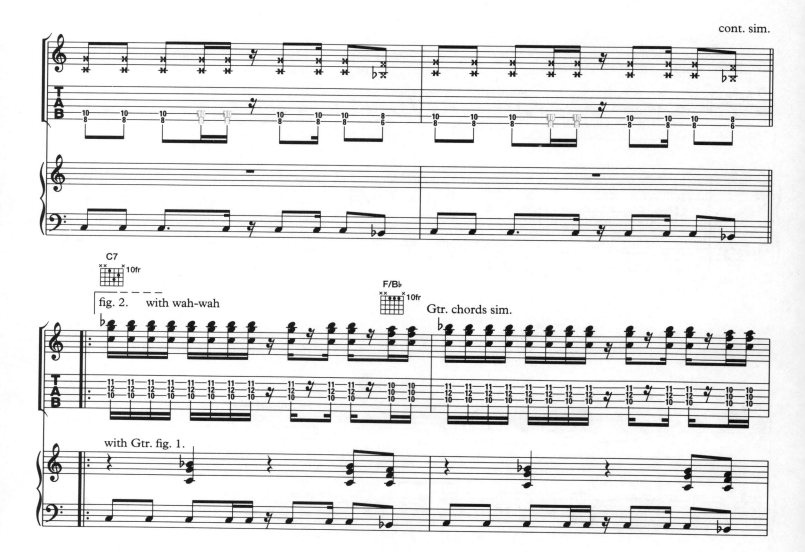

Ev - ery war _____ has been _____ done be - fore _____ and ev - ery - bo - dy _____ knows the pain.

The on - ly _____ one I know _____ ne - ver cries ne - ver o - pens your eyes. _____
The on - ly _____ one I see _____ is mine _____ when she walks down the street. _____

fig. 3.

cont. sim

gliss.

With Gtr. fig. 2

Tellin' Stories

Words and Music by Timothy Burgess, Martin Blunt, Robert Collins, Jon Brookes and Mark Collins

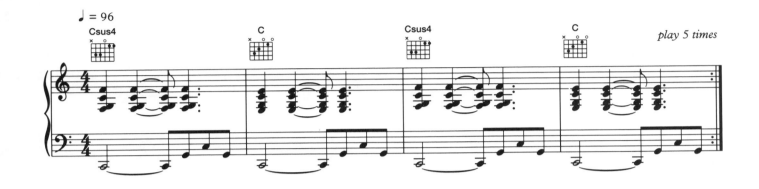

be there in the morn - ing, can't you see I'm tell - in' stor - ies, my sweet
see me in the morn - ing, can't you see I'm tell - in' stor - ies, my sweet

leaves fall to the ground, turn to brown___ through the day___ just like_____ you.
lead you to the top,___ don't stop,___ I could lead___ you there_____ still.

Live for the day,

_ I see your heart___ is emp - ty, I've___ got plen - ty. Joe___

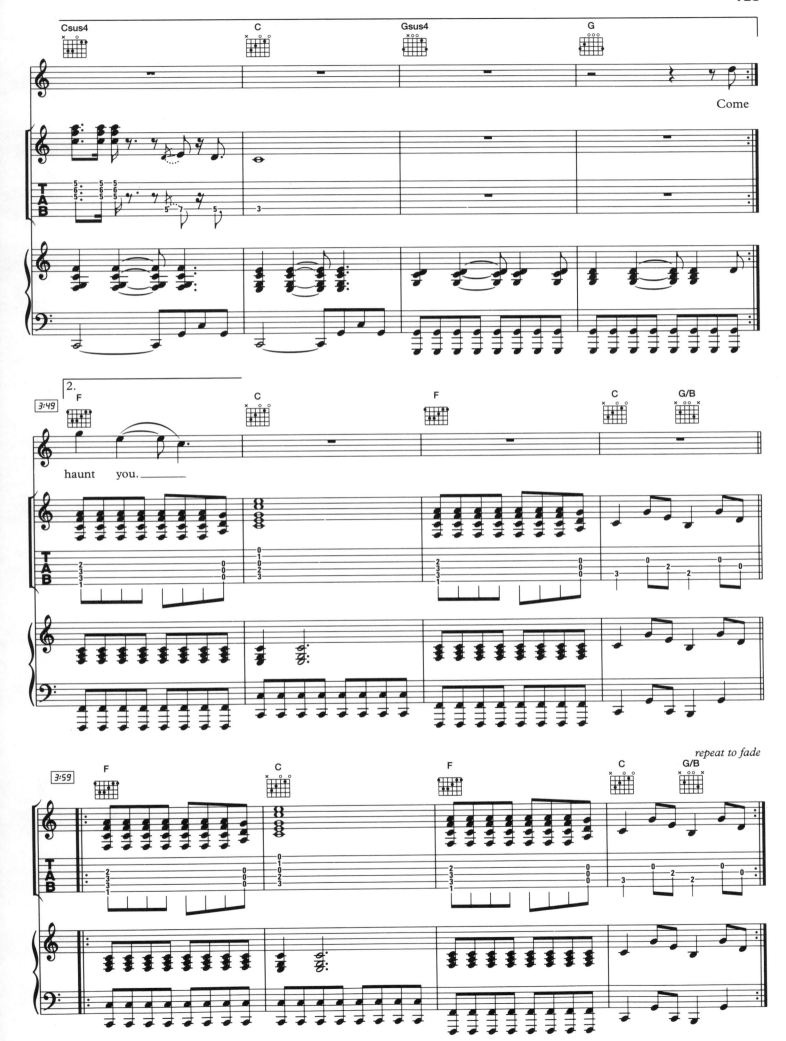

Then

Words and Music by Timothy Burgess, Martin Blunt, Robert Collins and Jon Brookes

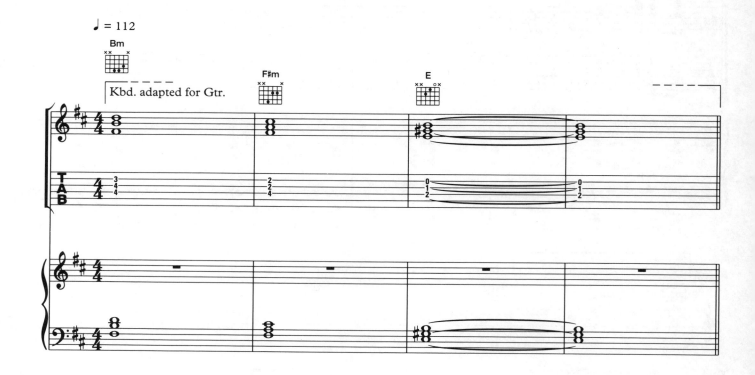

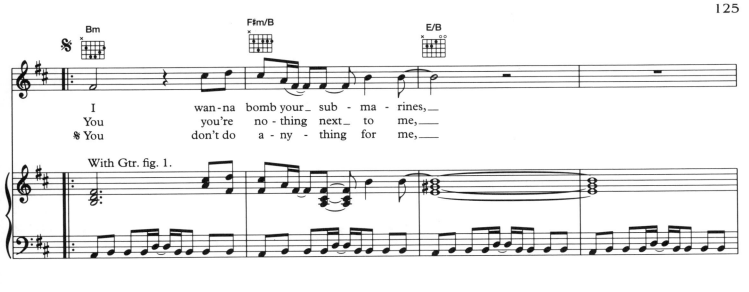

I wan-na bomb your sub-ma-rines,
You you're no-thing next to me,
You don't do a-ny-thing for me,

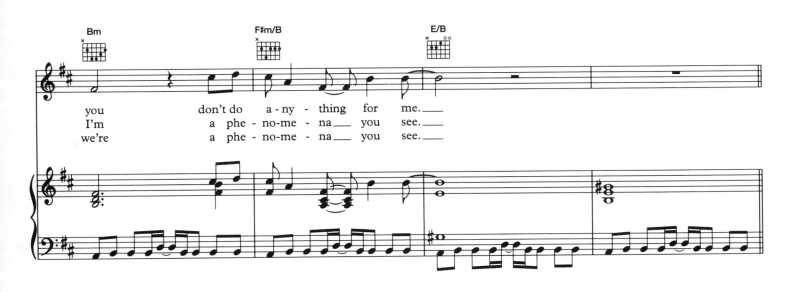

you don't do a-ny-thing for me.
I'm a phe-no-me-na you see.
we're a phe-no-me-na you see.

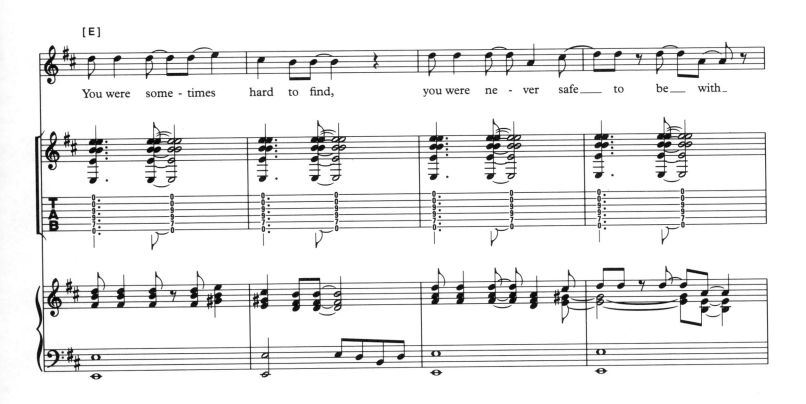

[E]

You were some-times hard to find, you were ne-ver safe to be with

Try Again Today

Words and Music by Timothy Burgess, Jon Brookes, Martin Blunt, Mark Collins, Anthony Rogers and James Dots

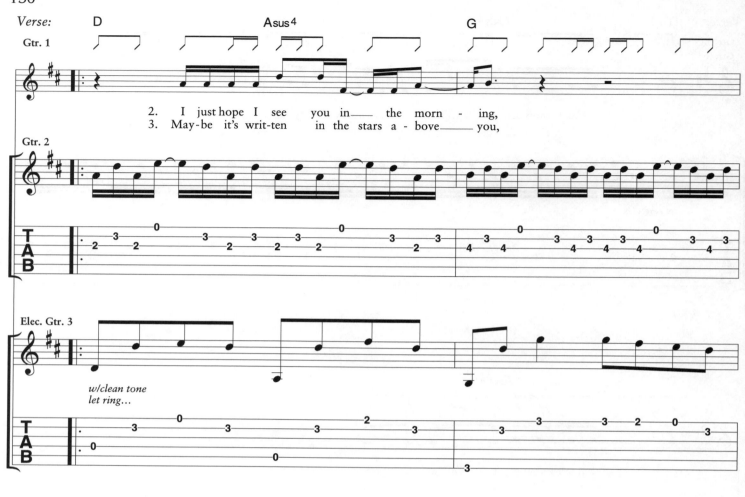

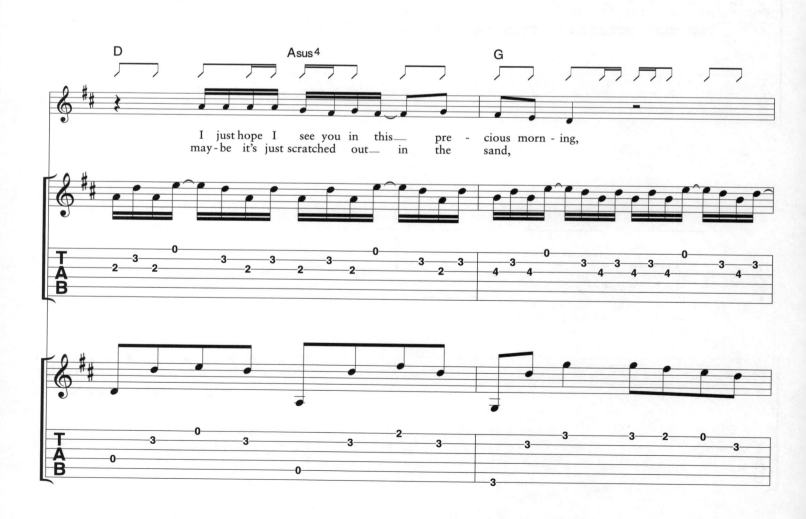

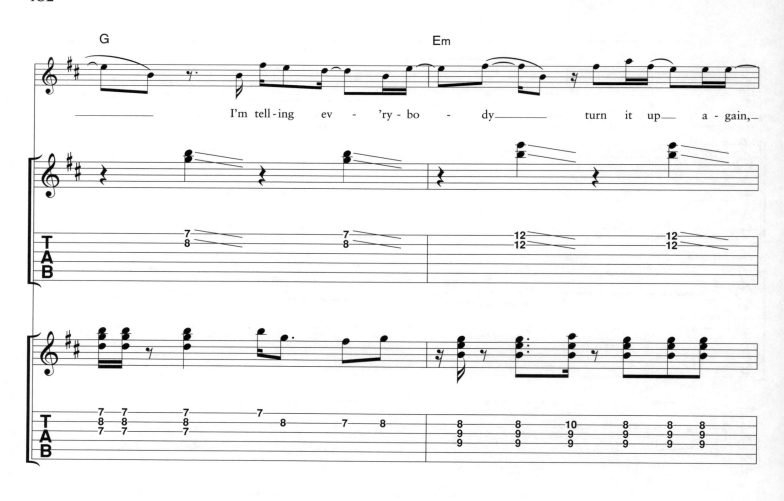

I'm tell-ing ev - 'ry-bo - dy_____ turn it up_ a - gain,

some-thing's got - ta change,_____ good-bye yes-ter-day,_

try a-gain to-day, some-thing's got-ta change.

let ring...

1.

Gtr. 2

w/clean tone
let ring...
w/Fig. 2 (1st 2 bars only)

Solo:

Cont. rhy. simile

Gtr. 2

let ring...

Gtr. 3

let ring...

D.%. al Coda

I'm gon-na try a-gain to-day.

Gtr. 2

let ring...

Up At The Lake

Words and Music by Timothy Burgess, Jon Brookes, Martin Blunt, Mark Collins and Anthony Rogers

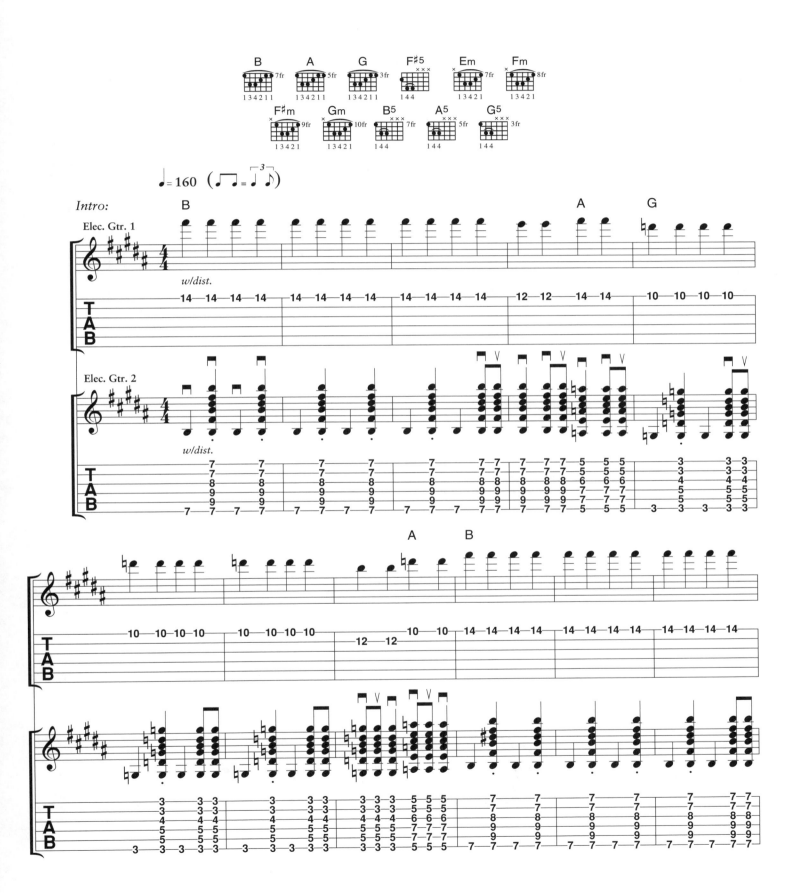

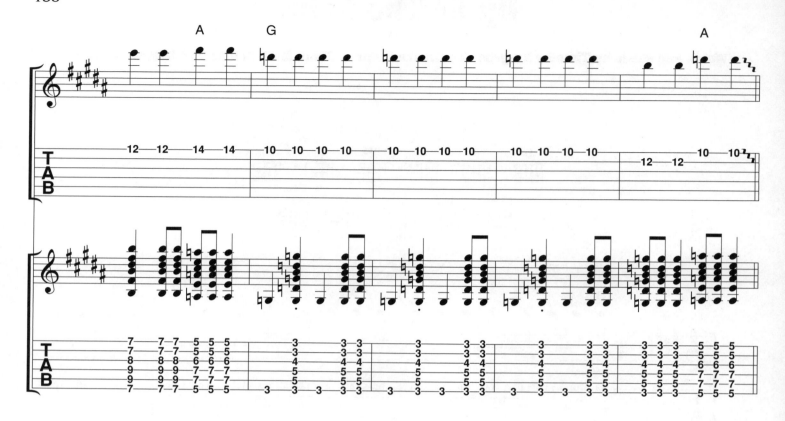

Verse:

B

1. I don't see no wheat fields from my win - dow to - day,_____
2. I know I've got a hand - ful, and I'm done, fit to burst,_____

(Verse 3 see block lyric)

tacet 1°
let ring...
Fig. 1

end Fig. 1

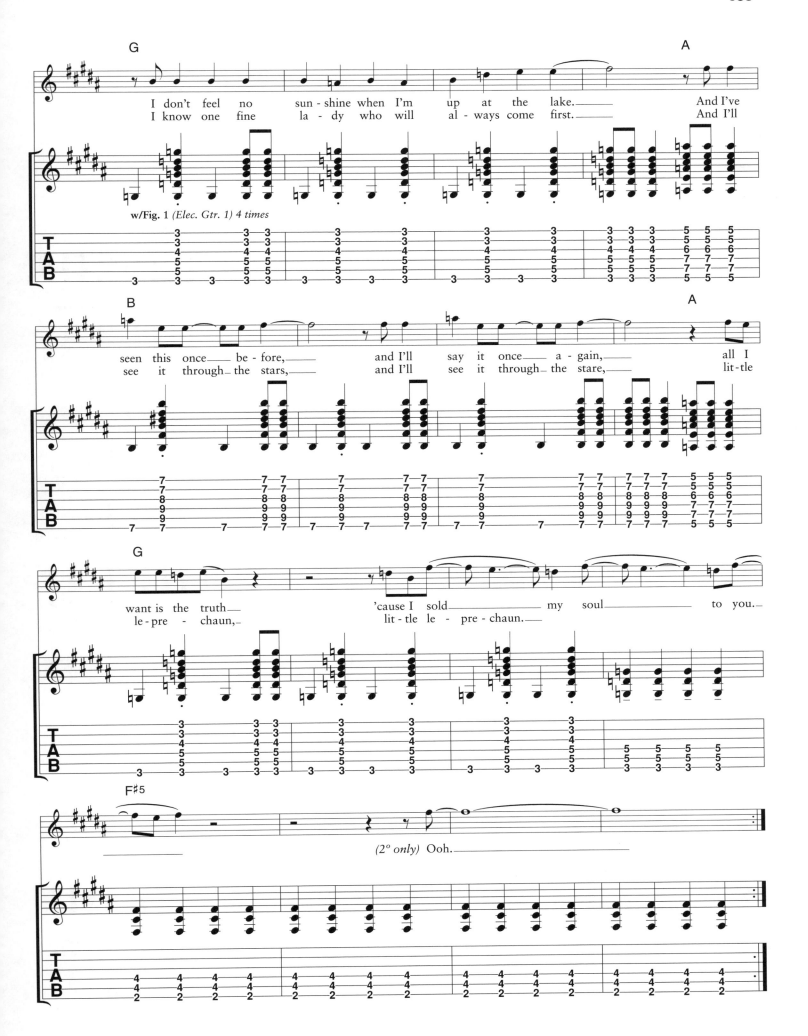

142

Verse 3:
I don't feel no pleasure when there's only a pain
I like a hit of bugle with a toot of champagne
You've seen me on fire
And you've seen me borderline
There is a world.

Weirdo

Words and Music by Timothy Burgess, Martin Blunt, Robert Collins and Jon Brookes

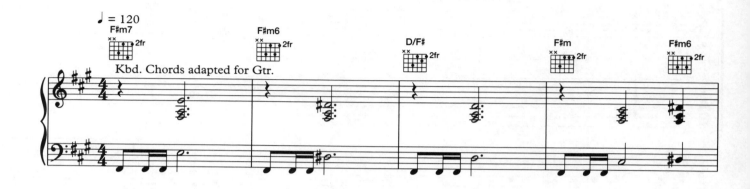

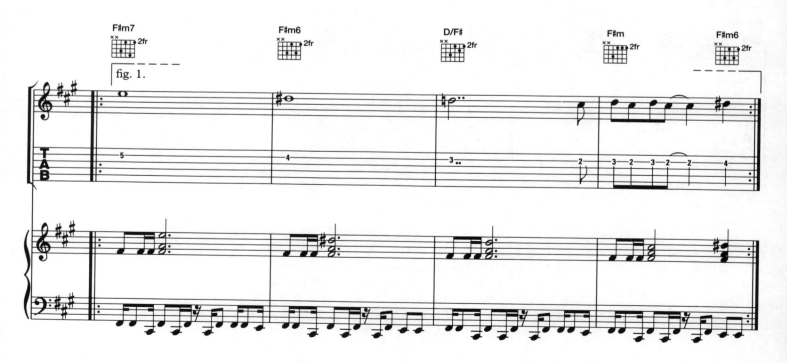

© **1992 Warner/Chappell Music Ltd, London W6 8BS**

look at your＿ ug - ly shame,＿ there's too much for me to know a-bout.

CODA

there's too much   for me to know   a-bout.

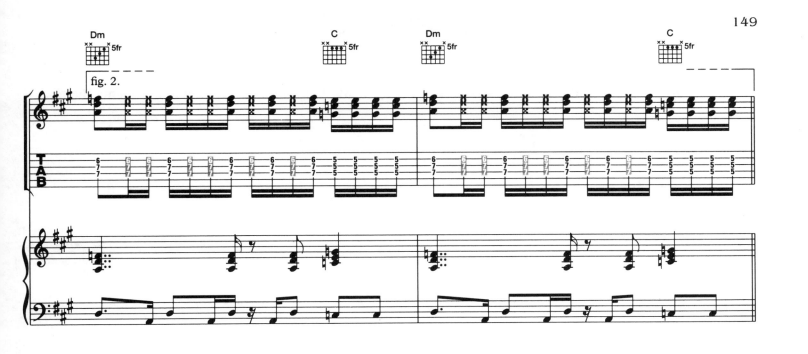

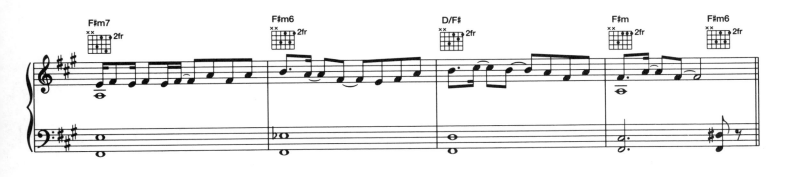

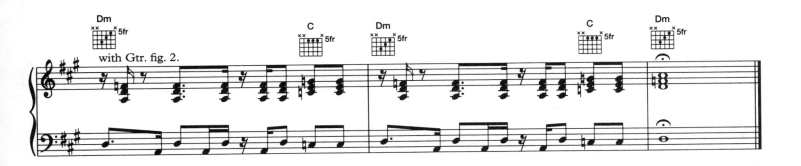

You're So Pretty - We're So Pretty

Words and Music by Timothy Burgess, Jon Brookes, Martin Blunt, Mark Collins and Anthony Rogers

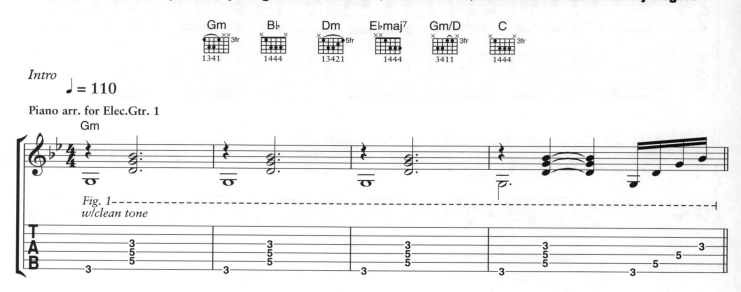

Intro
♩ = 110

Piano arr. for Elec.Gtr. 1

Fig. 1
w/clean tone

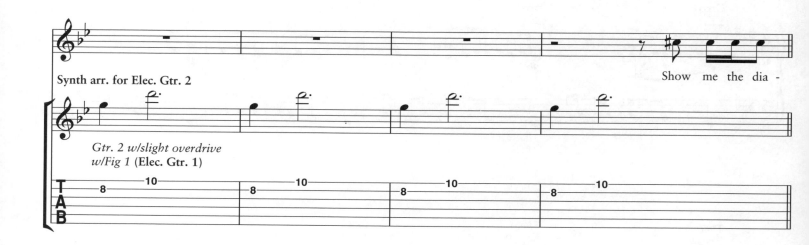

Synth arr. for Elec. Gtr. 2

Gtr. 2 w/slight overdrive
w/Fig 1 (Elec. Gtr. 1)

Show me the dia-

Verse 1

-monds, Show me the gold.___ Call me the an-swer, oh___ yeah.___

Elec. Gtr. 1

w/clean tone

Call me a - ny - where, I don't have a care,__ this is my__ world.__ You're so pret -

Bb   Dm   Gm

Chorus

Gtr. 1

- ty,   We're so pret - ty.

Elec. Gtr. 2

Gtr. 1 cont. in slashes
w/clean tone
Fig. 2

Elec. Gtr. 2

Fig. 3
Gtr. 2 w/slight overdrive
Gtr. 1 ad lib.

𝄋 *Verses 2 & 3*

Gm

2. Show me the sil - ver,   Show me the gold.__   You're tak - ing my name__
(3.) Ask - ing__ ques - tions.   Could - 'nt fit in.__

Elec. Gtr. 1

Gtr. 1 w/clean tone
Gtr. 2 w/Fig. 3

Talk-ing me to hell,___ for your sweet___ touch.
al-ways be the same,___ when there's a rain - bow.

You're so pret-

Chorus

Gtr. 1

- ty, We're so pret-ty.

You're so

Elec. Gtr. 2

Gtr. 2 w/slight overdrive

pret-ty, Oh so___ pret-ty.___

w/Fig 2 (Elec. Gtr. 3 clean)

1° *Drums only*
2° *w/Fig. 1* (**Elec. Gtr. 1 clean**), *w/fig 3.* (**Elec. Gtr. 2 overdrive**)

Show___ me the mo - ney. Show me the mo - ney ba - by.

To Coda ⊕

Show___ me the mo - ney. Show me the mo - ney ba - by.

Show___ me the mo - ney. Show me the mo - ney ba - by
You're so pret-

Elec. Gtr. 3

w/clean tone

Chorus

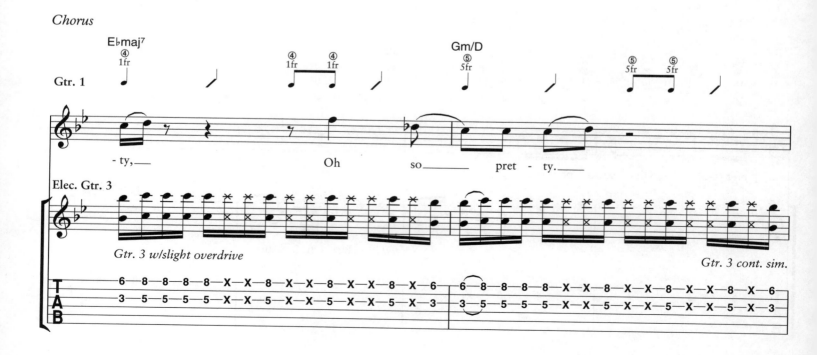

E♭maj⁷   Gm/D

Gtr. 1

- ty,___ Oh so___ pret - ty.___

Elec. Gtr. 3

Gtr. 3 w/slight overdrive

Gtr. 3 cont. sim.

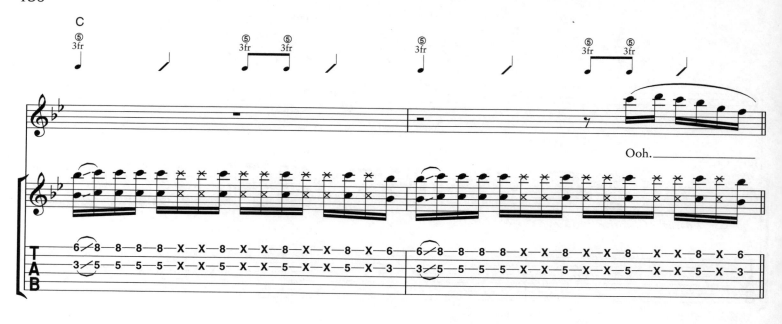

Outro

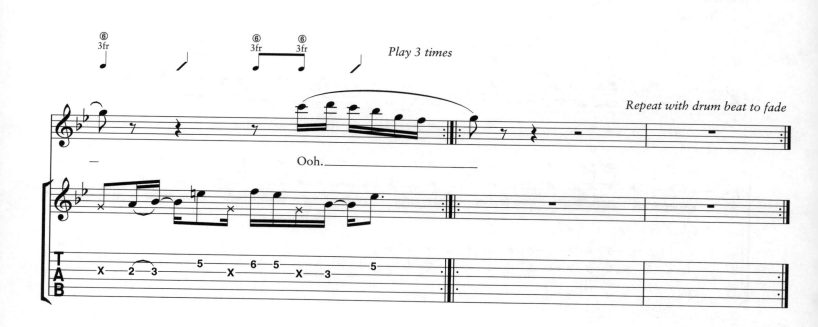